This
David Bennett Book
belongs to

_____

_____

_____

_____

_____

To Lisa, Pod
G. P-R.

First published in 1993 by
David Bennett Books Ltd,
94 Victoria Street, St Albans,
Herts, AL1 3TG

BRITISH LIBRARY CATALOGUING IN PUBLICATION DATA
A catalogue record for this book is available
from the British Library
ISBN 1 85602 027 4

Typesetting by Type City
Production by Imago
Printed in Hong Kong

No Such Thing as Monsters

Guy Parker-Rees

David Bennett Books

'I've never seen a monster. I want to see a real monster!' demanded Wilf.

'All right,' said his Mum and she took him to see . . .

A monster.

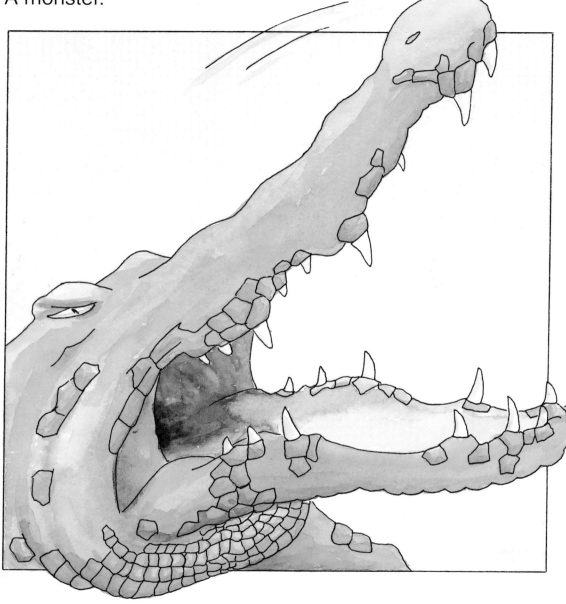

'That's not a monster – that's a crocodile.
I want to see a *real* monster,' yelled Wilf.

'All right,' said his Mum, and she took him to see . . .

A monster.

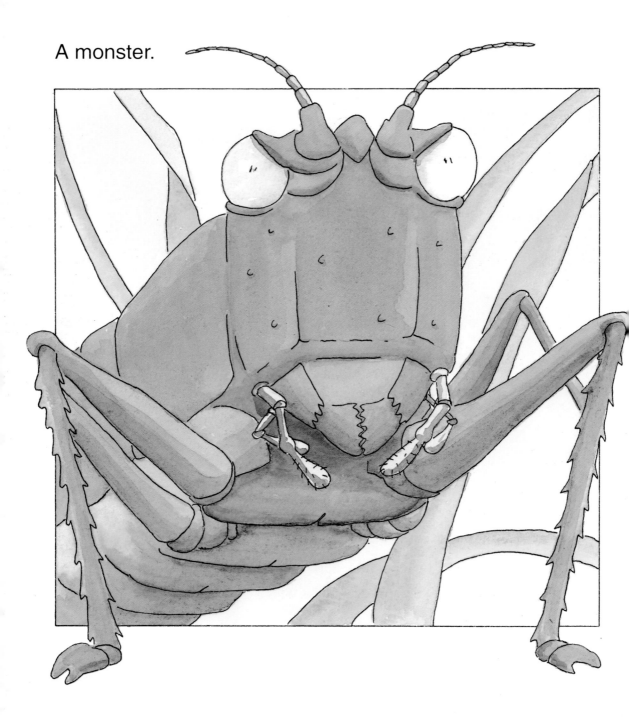

'That's not a monster – that's a grasshopper under a magnifying glass,' stomped Wilf.
'I want to see a monster that wobbles and slobbers and goes BLEAUGGHHH!'

'Just wait here,' sighed his Mum.
Wilf waited. Soon he heard a wobble, then a slobber, and a . . .

'That's not a monster – it's you in disguise.
I want to see a *real* monster!'
'All right then . . .'

And she took him to see . . .

A monster.

'But that's just a model dinosaur.'
'I give up,' groaned Wilf's Mum.
'Look for a monster yourself.'
    Wilf threw a pebble into the sea.

'Take me over there then,' he said,
pointing to a small rocky island.

They found a boat, and off they rowed. Wilf's Mum
heaved at the oars, as Wilf trailed his finger in the sea.

'Don't go too far,' called his Mum,
and she flopped down for a rest.

Wilf searched for
snoozing seabeasts
in deep cool pools.

He searched for
dozing dragons
in dark damp caves,
until, at last, behind
a rock, he saw . . .

A monster!
Wilf hurled his rope to catch it.
  'Got you!' he cried.

'Agggh!' bellowed the fisherman mending his net.
'Oops,' gulped Wilf as he scampered off over the rocks.
He ran and ran and ran as fast as his bendy legs
would carry him.

'Now which is the way back?' panted Wilf
when he couldn't run any more.
He searched and searched, but it was no good.
He was lost.

Wilf felt tired and lonely.
He crawled under an upturned old boat.
It made him feel like a tortoise, safe in his shell.
He watched the moon rise quietly in the sky.

But slowly, everything began to look scary.
Nobbly heads and bobbly noses
bulged out of the clouds.

Slimies and slitheries squirmed out of the sea.

Aagh! Horrible hairies were about
to pounce on him from the rocks.

'They've got me!' he cried, as he felt something
pulling at his leg.

'I've found you at last,' said Wilf's Mum,
scooping him up and giving him a big hug.
'I wish you wouldn't go running off like that!'

'I . . . I thought you were a horrible hairy rock monster,' stammered Wilf as they set off back to the boat.

'Don't be silly,' said Wilf's Mum . . .

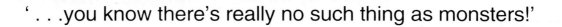

' . . .you know there's really no such thing as monsters!'

Have you collected all these *Sparklers*

The Terrible Troll *Andy Cooke*   ISBN 1 85602 030 4
The last troll alive is terrorising young Alice's town.
Everyone flees for their lives. Who can save them?

The Boy Who Ate The Sun *Jon Cramer*   ISBN 1 85602 028 2
A little boy loves the sun so much that he decides to eat it.
But things don't turn out quite as he expects!

Barnyard Bash *Tessa Richardson-Jones*   ISBN 1 85602 025 8
When the farmer and his family go out for the day,
their animals decide to have some fun!

The Purrfect Carpet *David Passes • Norman Johnson*   ISBN 1 85602 029 0
Twopence loves Princess Purrfect dearly, but he is so poor – how can he ever win her hand?

Bed Bugs *Stuart Trotter*   ISBN 1 85602 026 6
When Tommy hears noises *inside* his bed, he decides
to investigate – and makes some curious discoveries!

No Such Thing As Monsters *Guy Parker-Rees*   ISBN 1 85602 027 4
'There's no such thing as monsters,' says Wilf's Mum. But is that true?

Float and Sink

Written by Maria Gordon
and
Illustrated by Mike Gordon

Wayland

Simple Science

JS32.2

Air
Colour
Day and Night
Heat
Electricity and Magnetism
Float and Sink

Light
Materials
Push and Pull
Rocks and Soil
Skeletons and Movement
Sound

Series Editor: Catherine Baxter
Advice given by: Audrey Randall - member of the Science Working Group
for the National Curriculum.

This edition published in 1995 by
Wayland (Publishers) Ltd

First published in 1994 by
Wayland (Publishers) Ltd
61 Western Road, Hove
East Sussex, BN3 1JD, England

British Library Cataloguing in Publication Data
Gorden, Maria
 Float and Sink. - (Simple Science Series)
 I. Title II. Gordon, Mike III. Series 532

HARDBACK ISBN 0-7502-1284-5
PAPERBACK ISBN 0-7502-1727-8

Typeset by Liz Miller, Wayland (Publishers) Ltd
Printed and bound in Italy by G Canale

Contents

Some things float.
They stay on top of water.

A duck floats on a pond.

Some things sink. They go down in water.

An egg sinks in a pond.

What things float? What things sink?
Are they heavy or light?
What shape are they?

Ask a grown up to fill a
big bowl with water.

6

Put different objects in
the water.

You could try using an orange, a
brick, a cork, a marble, an egg,
a coin, a pencil, a nail, a wood-
en spoon, a rubber, a candle, a
china bowl, a china plate, a
sponge and a small ball.

Find two small plastic bottles the same size.
Fill one right up with water or sand to make
it heavy.

Put on the lids.
Put one on each hand.
Can you feel the heavy
bottle pushing down
on your hand?

See which bottle floats and
which one sinks.

When you put things in water they push down on it.

Heavy things push down more.

But water pushes things back up. This is called upthrust.

If you push a small balloon under water and let it go, the upthrust pushes the balloon back up.

Things which sink push down
harder than the water pushes up.

10

Things which float don't push down
as hard as the water pushes up.
So the water holds them up.

Some things which are not heavy push down hard on water.

We say they are dense. A pin is dense. It isn't heavy but it sinks.

Yikes!

Some heavy things do not
push down hard on water.
They are not very dense.
A log isn't dense.
It's heavy but it floats.

Air does not push down hard on water. There is air inside an empty plastic bottle, so it floats. Sand pushes down hard on water.

If you fill a bottle with sand, it sinks.

Tyres are filled with air.

Do you think they float?

You can make some things
float and sink.
Put a lump of Plasticine
the size of a tennis
ball into a large bowl
of water.

What happens?

Now make it into the
shape of a bowl.

What happens
this time?

The lump of Plasticine pushes down on a small bit of the water so it sinks. The bowl-shaped Plasticine pushes down on a bigger bit of water. The water can push up more of the Plasticine and hold it up so the bowl floats.

Ouch!

Make different Plasticine bowl shapes. How many marbles can they hold before they sink?

Too many marbles push down harder than the water can push up.
They make the plasticine bowls too heavy.

What happens if you put marbles only on one side of a bowl?

Why is one boat sinking?

Cork

Wax

insects

Wood

bananas

People used to think ships could only be made from things that float. But a man called Mr Brunel showed people that things that sink can be made to float.

A lump of iron will sink.
But Mr Brunel made a very
big ship out of iron. This ship
showed that dense things can
float if you change their shape.

Use coloured sticky tape to
mark the water level in a
large bowl.

Put a lump of Plasticine
in the water.

The water
level goes up.

Do the same with a Plasticine bowl.
The water level goes up even more.

When things make water move up
it is called displacement.

A man called Archimedes lived a long, long time ago in Greece. He found out about displacement. He saw it happen when he got into his bath.

He jumped out of the bath and ran out shouting 'Eureka!' This means 'I have found it!' People said he was so pleased he forgot to put on his clothes!

See how much the water moves up when you have a bath!

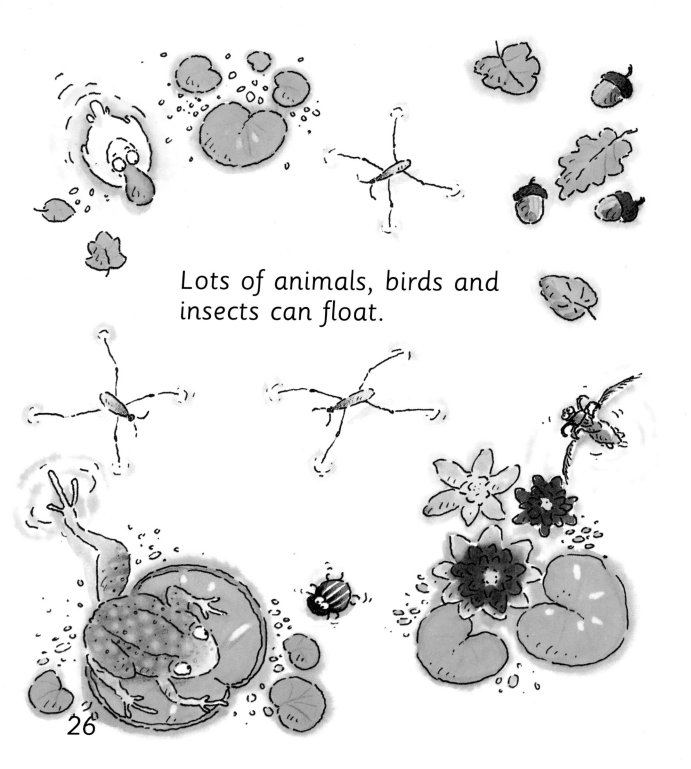

Lots of animals, birds and insects can float.

26

Things that can swim know how to move so they can stop themselves sinking.

Things that float or sink
can help us.

How many can you find in
the picture?

29

Notes for adults

The 'Simple Science' series helps children to reach Keystage 1: Attainment targets 1-4 of the Science National Curriculum. Below are some suggestions to help complement and extend the learning in this book.

7   Try using a peeled orange and a bad egg.

8/9   Feel the weight of two identical, unopened cans suspended on string - one immersed in water.

12/13   Use pictures and real objects to make a display of fishing floats, anchors, buoys etc. Compare properties of living things and inanimate objects. Make lolly stick rafts. Write a story about the pictures.

14   Measure different amounts of sand, eg half a bottle, quarter of a bottle. How much sand is needed before the bottle sinks?

16/17   Investigate boats around the world from kayaks and sampans, to paddle boats and oil tankers.

18/19   Experiment with loads of objects of different densities and weights. Investigate the Plimsoll line on ships. Make up a rhyme or song about the picture.

20/21   Explore the history of boats in different countries. Look at the effects of modern shipping - its advantages

(eg transport) and disadvantages (eg oil spills).
Investigate uses of floating and sinking in different
cultures and in history - from apple bobbing to
witch ducking.

22/23 Read Aesop's fable of the crow, the water and the stones.

24/25 Read the original story of Archimedes and the gold and
silver crowns. Investigate his inventions.

26/27 Investigate salt water. Go swimming!

28/29 In groups, make wall friezes showing floating and sinking.
How many different things can each group illustrate? Do a
project on water safety. Make ice-cream floats.

Other books to read

Keep it Afloat by J. Rowe and M. Perham (Watts, 1993)

My Boat by K. Davies and W. Oldfield (A & C Black, 1990)

Submarines by Tim Wood (Franklin Watts, 1989)

Floating & Sinking by K. Davies and W. Oldfield
(Wayland, 1990)

Floating & Sinking, *Into Science* series
(Oxford Primary Books, 1994)

Index